COUNT THE CROP

Tito and ~~their~~ gather the tomatoes their father planted in the spring. Can you tell how many tomatoes they have altogether?

Hint on page 46

Illustration: Rick Geary

1 DOZEN TOMATOES

1 DOZEN TOMATOES
1 DOZEN TOMATOES
1 DOZEN TOMATOES
1 DOZEN TOMATOES

1 DOZEN TOMATOES
1 DOZEN TOMATOES
1 DOZEN TOMATOES
1 DOZEN TOMATOES

Answer on page 48

SPECIAL DELIVERIES

Help Hannah deliver each package to the correct house.

33

35

31

40 – 4

5 × 5 + 5

16 + 16

20 + 14

7 × 5

44 – 7

11 × 3

14 + 13 + 12

41 – 8 – 2

Answer on page 48

10 + 19 + 9

Do the problems on the packages to find the proper addresses.

Hint on page 46

Illustration: Scott Peck

STRAIGHT RUNS

Don't go racing off before you find three consecutive numbers that will answer each question below.

1. The sum of three consecutive numbers is 18. What are the numbers?

2. The sum of three consecutive numbers is 39. What are the numbers?

3. The sum of three consecutive numbers is 72. What are the numbers?

4. The sum of three consecutive numbers is 90. What are the numbers?

BONUS QUESTION:

The total of three consecutive numbers is the same whether the three numbers are added together or multiplied. What are the numbers, and what is that total?

Answer on page 48

Hint on page 46

Illustration: Rick Geary

6

WONDER WINDOW

Hint on page 46

Are there more squares or triangles in this window?

Illustration: Jason Thorne

ZOO CLUES

Hedd County has grown so much that the county officials split the zoo into four smaller ones. Each new zoo has an exhibit of exotic animals. Every zoo is supposed to have four of each animal, but the totals aren't quite even yet.

NUMBER OF ANIMALS PER ZOO				
	How's by Zoo	Can Zoo	Watt's Zoo	Because of Zoo
Alligator	5	3	4	4
Python	2	4	5	5
Toucan	4	2	4	6
Gorilla	5	6	4	1
Elephant	3	5	5	3
Giraffe	1	2	7	6

The zoos are about to distribute the animals so that each zoo will have an equal number. Can you help the zookeepers decide how they should move some of the animals around?

STACKING STANLEY

Stanley has to stack these boxes according to size, with the longest box on the bottom and the shortest box on the top. If you help him figure out which box goes where, the letters on the sides should tell you what is in the boxes.

Illustration: R. Michael Palan

Hint on page 46

H G F N J O S O N

DOTS
A LOT

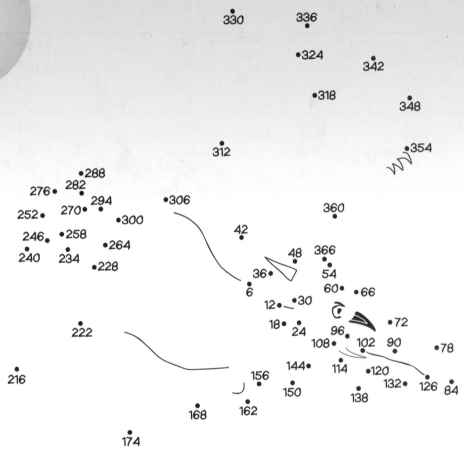

330

336

•324

342

•318

348

312

•354

•288
282
276•
294
270•
252•
•300
246•
•258
•264
240 234
•228

•306

360

42

48 366
36•
54
6
60• •66
12• •30
•72
18• •24
96
108• •102 90
222
144• 114 •78
216
156
•120
150
132• 126 84
138
168
162
174

198

210

204

192 186 180•

Illustration: John Puntar

IT'S ABOUT TIME

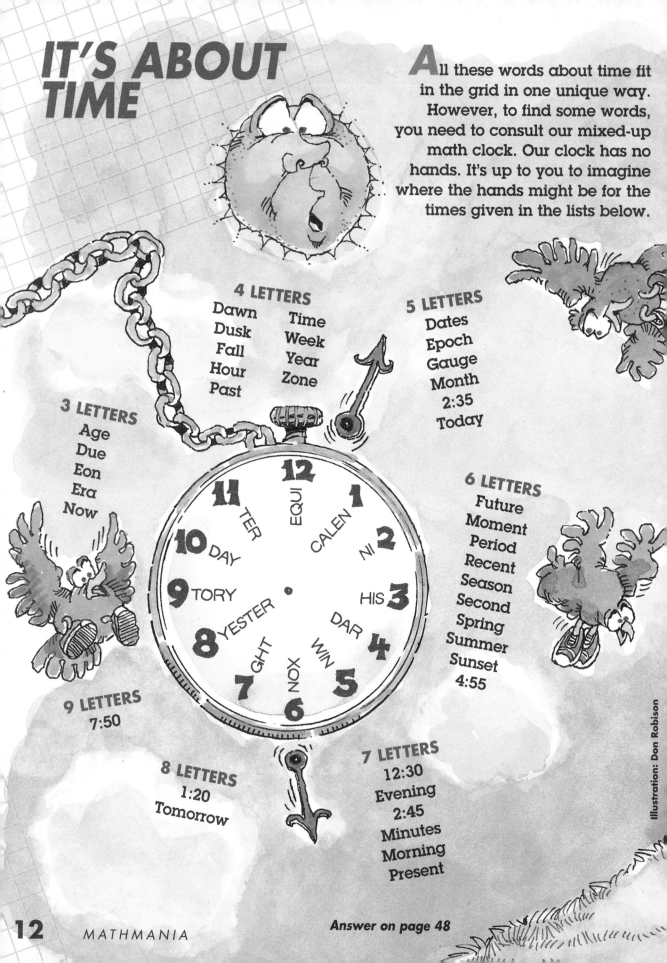

All these words about time fit in the grid in one unique way. However, to find some words, you need to consult our mixed-up math clock. Our clock has no hands. It's up to you to imagine where the hands might be for the times given in the lists below.

4 LETTERS
Dawn
Dusk
Fall
Hour
Past
Time
Week
Year
Zone

5 LETTERS
Dates
Epoch
Gauge
Month
2:35
Today

3 LETTERS
Age
Due
Eon
Era
Now

6 LETTERS
Future
Moment
Period
Recent
Season
Second
Spring
Summer
Sunset
4:55

9 LETTERS
7:50

8 LETTERS
1:20
Tomorrow

7 LETTERS
12:30
Evening
2:45
Minutes
Morning
Present

Clock labels:
12 EQUI
1 CALEN
2 NI
3 HIS
4 DAR
5 WIN
6 NOX
7 GHT
8 YESTER
9 TORY
10 DAY
11 TER

Illustration: Don Robison

Answer on page 48

When you correctly combine the letters at the spots where the two hands point, you'll get a new word. The smaller hour hand always points to the first part of the word. The minute hand always points to the end of the word.

For example, under the category 7 LETTERS, you'll see the time of 12:30. On the clock, you'll find EQUI at the 12 and NOX at the 6, which combine to spell EQUINOX, the time when the sun crosses the equator.

Hint on page 46

PHONE AGE

Before leaving summer camp, Jed and some of his camp mates exchanged telephone numbers in the 000 area code. As he was riding home, he noticed an odd coincidence. Each camper's phone number added up to his or her age. Can you match the friends to their phone numbers?

Sylvia, age 14
Oliver, age 15
Jaime, age 7
Lara, age 8
Ari, age 11
Bruce, age 12
Lola, age 9
Joel, age 16
Nate, age 10
Ellis, age 13

802-1005
521-0600
233-1202
410-2102
203-0002
310-0050
202-4000
614-3001
321-1103
401-3121

Illustration: Bill Colrus

Hint on page 46

Answer on page 48

GRAPHIX

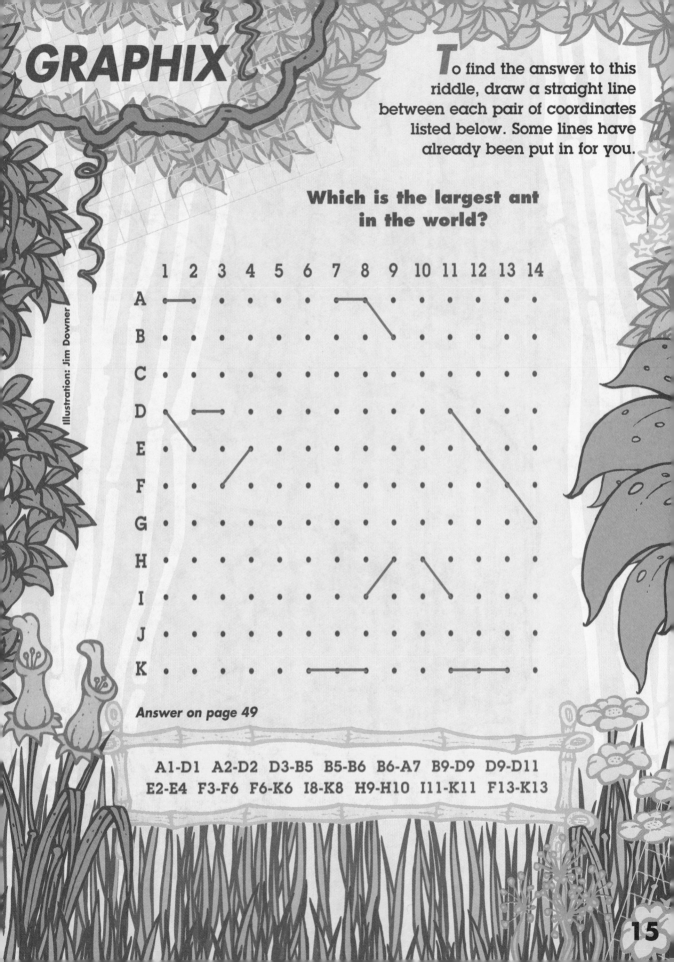

To find the answer to this riddle, draw a straight line between each pair of coordinates listed below. Some lines have already been put in for you.

Which is the largest ant in the world?

Answer on page 49

A1-D1 A2-D2 D3-B5 B5-B6 B6-A7 B9-D9 D9-D11
E2-E4 F3-F6 F6-K6 I8-K8 H9-H10 I11-K11 F13-K13

15

SQUARE 100

*T*he kids are trying to figure out how to fill in the blanks of the grid that Kerri just drew. The numbers in each group of four adjacent squares must total 100.

Hint on page 46

Illustration: Joe Boddy

Numbers may appear more than once. For example, in Bernice's smaller grid, the numbers in each adjacent square equal 100.

Now hop to it and see how long it takes you to fill in the big grid.

25	35	15
10	30	20
15	45	5

CUTUPS

Lumber Jackie has a pole that is 90 feet long. She wants to cut it into nine equal pieces of 10 feet each. How many cuts will she need to make?

Illustration: Rocky Fuller

Answer on page 49

BUSY DAY

Jennifer is planning to do a lot on Saturday. She's already filled in most of her planner. But she has a few other things she needs to find time for. Help her out by putting each task into a time slot. All the items will fit to give Jen a full day.

SATURDAY

7:40 a.m. Wake up. Put on sweats—should take 5 minutes.

8:00 a.m. Eat breakfast.

8:15 a.m. Shower and get dressed. Put wash into machine before leaving.

8:30 a.m. Leave for 45-minute drive to Beverly's house.

9:30 a.m. Help Beverly paint her room—should take 3 hours.

12:30 p.m. Go to lunch for an hour.

2:05 p.m. Go home.

3:00 p.m. Go shopping with Mom—should take 90 minutes.

5:20 p.m. Weed front garden—should take 40 minutes.

6:10 p.m. Write thank-you note to Mrs. Tillson—should take 5 minutes.

7:15 p.m. Eat dinner with family.

7:40 p.m. Wash dishes—should take 20 minutes.

8:15 p.m. Leave for the movies.

10:30 p.m. Come home and go to sleep. Big day tomorrow!

Still to do:
Walk the dog twice (15 minutes each).
Hang out the wash (10 minutes).
Get haircut (45 minutes).
Wash cars (1 hour).
Write letter to Carl (30 minutes).

Illustration: Bill Colrus

Answer on page 49

DIGIT DOES IT

That amazing investigator, Inspector Digit, is hot on the trail of an ice-cream crook. Someone took all the cones from Softee's Sweets.

Illustration: Joe Boddy

The only clue is a coded note. Can you decipher the note, find the clues, and help the Inspector lick this case?

‾‾ ‾ ‾ ‾‾   ‾ ‾ ‾‾ ‾‾ ‾ ‾‾ ‾ ‾ ‾‾   ‾‾ ‾ ‾‾ ‾ ‾'
11 4 5 15   3 8 18 13 4 10 7 2 15   11 3 20 3 7

‾‾ ‾   ‾ ‾ ‾ ‾   ‾‾ ‾ ‾ ‾   ‾ ‾ ‾
18 2   7 9 4 6   18 4 8 7   7 9 4

‾‾ ‾‾ ‾ ‾ ‾‾   ‾ ‾‾   ‾ ‾ ‾   ‾‾ ‾ ‾‾ ‾‾
10 15 4 5 19   2 17   7 9 4   10 2 13 18

‾ ‾‾ ‾ ‾ ‾‾   ‾‾ ‾   ‾ ‾ ‾‾   ‾‾ ‾‾ ‾ ‾ ‾'
5 17 7 4 15   19 4   9 2 22   18 22 4 4 7

‾‾ ‾ ‾   ‾‾ ‾   ‾ ‾‾ ‾ ‾ ‾‾   ‾‾ ‾ ‾‾ ‾‾   ‾‾ ‾
21 1 7   19 6   7 15 5 3 16   22 3 16 16   21 4

‾‾ ‾ ‾‾ ‾‾   ‾‾ ‾ ‾‾ ‾ ‾‾ ‾   ‾ ‾ ‾
10 2 16 11   21 4 17 2 15 4   6 2 1

‾‾ ‾ ‾ ‾‾ ‾‾   ‾ ‾ ‾ ‾ ‾ ‾ ‾ ‾‾
18 7 3 10 12   5 8 6 7 9 3 8 20

‾ ‾   ‾‾ ‾.   ‾   ‾ ‾‾ ‾ ‾   ‾‾ ‾ ‾‾ ‾
2 8   19 4   3   4 14 4 8   16 4 17 7

O H   ‾ ‾‾ ‾   ‾‾ ‾‾ ‾ ‾ ‾‾   ‾‾ ‾ ‾ ‾‾ ‾‾ ‾‾
      3 10 4   10 15 4 5 19   18 7 3 10 12 18

‾‾ ‾ ‾ ‾ ‾ ‾‾   ‾‾ ‾   ‾ ‾ ‾   ‾‾ ‾ ‾ ‾,
21 4 9 3 8 11   18 2   6 2 1   22 2 8 7

‾‾ ‾ ‾‾   ‾ ‾‾ ‾ ‾ ‾‾   ‾‾ ‾.
13 2 13   5 17 7 4 15   19 4

‾‾ ‾ ‾‾ ‾‾ ‾   ‾‾ ‾ ‾ ‾‾ ‾ ‾‾
15 2 10 12 6   15 9 2 11 4 18

Answer on page 49

Hint on page 47

MATHMANIA 21

GOOD FENCES

Hint on page 47

The members of the 5-H club, Hillary, Hilda, Henry, Howie, and Horace, want to put a fence around this garden. It is 100 feet square. If they put the fence posts 10 feet away from one another, how many posts will they need to fence in this plot of land?

Illustration: John Nez

Answer on page 49

A DIRTY JOB

Peter's pickup can transport a maximum of 750 pounds per trip. How many trips will it take for him to remove the entire pile?

CLEAN FILL 6 TONS

Illustration: Michael Austin

Hint on page 47

Answer on page 49

23

AN AMAZING WOMAN

Sarah Josepha Hale contributed much to America. She lived from 1788 to 1879. Did you ever hear of her?

Thanks in part to her persuasion, President Abraham Lincoln declared the first national holiday, Thanksgiving Day, in 1863.

PROCLAMATION

THANKSGIVING DAY

A. Lincoln

In the mid-1800s, she was the editor of one of the nation's first women's magazines, *Godey's Lady's Book*, which was published for more than 35 years.

In 1830, she wrote a famous poem. To find the title, cross out the contents of the grid as instructed. Write the remaining letters, from left to right and top to bottom, in the blanks to reveal the name of the poem.

"

__ __ __ __ __ __ __ __

"

__ __ __ __ __ __ __ __ __ __

M	O	A	Q	C	U
S	K	F	Z	R	S
W	Y	G	P	O	H
P	X	V	U	N	W
A	S	D	$	C	A
K	P	Z	F	L	I
C	T	N	W	T	P
&	F	L	O	S	Q
S	E	G	C	L	A
U	F	M	W	B	P

Cross out
~ The fourth consonant of the alphabet
~ The only letter that must be followed by a vowel
~ The letter that is the fourth one down in the second column
~ The one letter that appears in the 3rd, 4th, 6th, 7th, and 10th rows
~ The last two full-time vowels
~ The consonants in the word *snack*
~ The only letter with a multisyllable name
~ The (7 + 6 + 5 + 4 + 3 + 1)th letter of the alphabet
~ The letters in the word *give*, except the vowels
~ Anything that is not a letter

Illustration: Rick Geary

DIFFERENT DEFINITIONS

You'll have to figure out our definition of today's word a piece at a time. Find the letters described by each clue. Then print the letters in the boxes, going from left to right in order.

Today's word: **WEEKDAYS**

First $\frac{1}{3}$ of THIRDS

Final $\frac{1}{3}$ of ARE

Final $\frac{5}{6}$ of HONEST

Final $\frac{3}{4}$ of CHAT

First $\frac{4}{5}$ of ARENA

First $\frac{3}{4}$ of TASK

First $\frac{1}{2}$ of STRING

Final $\frac{1}{2}$ of IRON

First $\frac{3}{8}$ of GASOLINE

First $\frac{5}{6}$ of SATURN

First $\frac{1}{3}$ of DOG

Final $\frac{4}{5}$ of MAYOR

First $\frac{4}{7}$ of SUNDIAL

Final $\frac{2}{3}$ of PAY

Illustration: R. Michael Palan

Answer on page 49

PATTERN POSSIBILITIES

Each shape contains a numbered pattern. Can you fill in the missing whole number in each design?

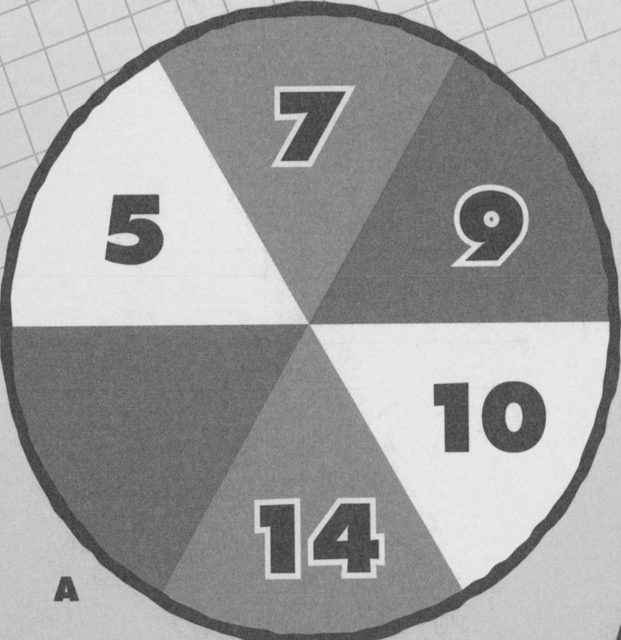

A

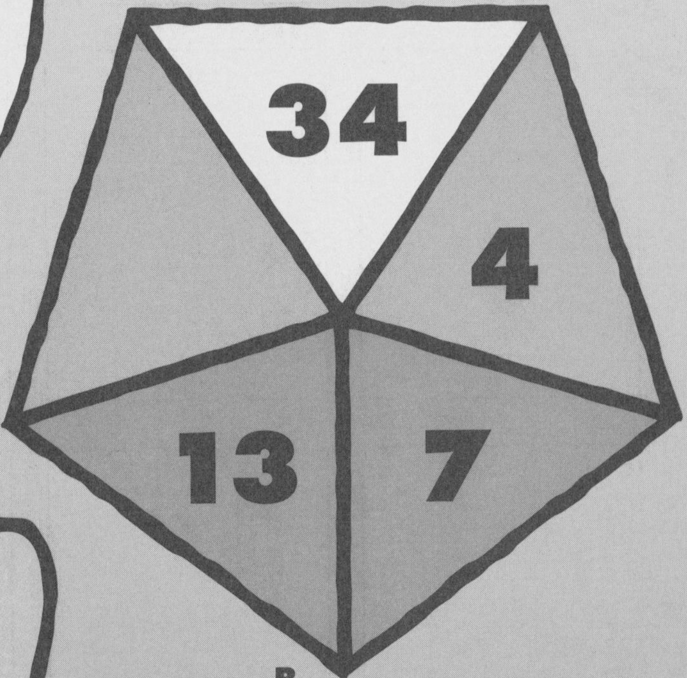

7

5

9

10

14

B

34

4

13

7

C

5

6

8

4

7

9

Answer on page 49

SCRAMBLED PICTURE

Copy these mixed-up rectangles onto the next page to unscramble the scene.

A-3 A-2 A-1 A-4

B-2 B-4 B-3 B-1

C-4 C-3 C-2 C-1

D-3 D-1 D-4 D-2

The letters and numbers
tell you where each rectangle
belongs. We've done the first
one, A-3, to start you off.

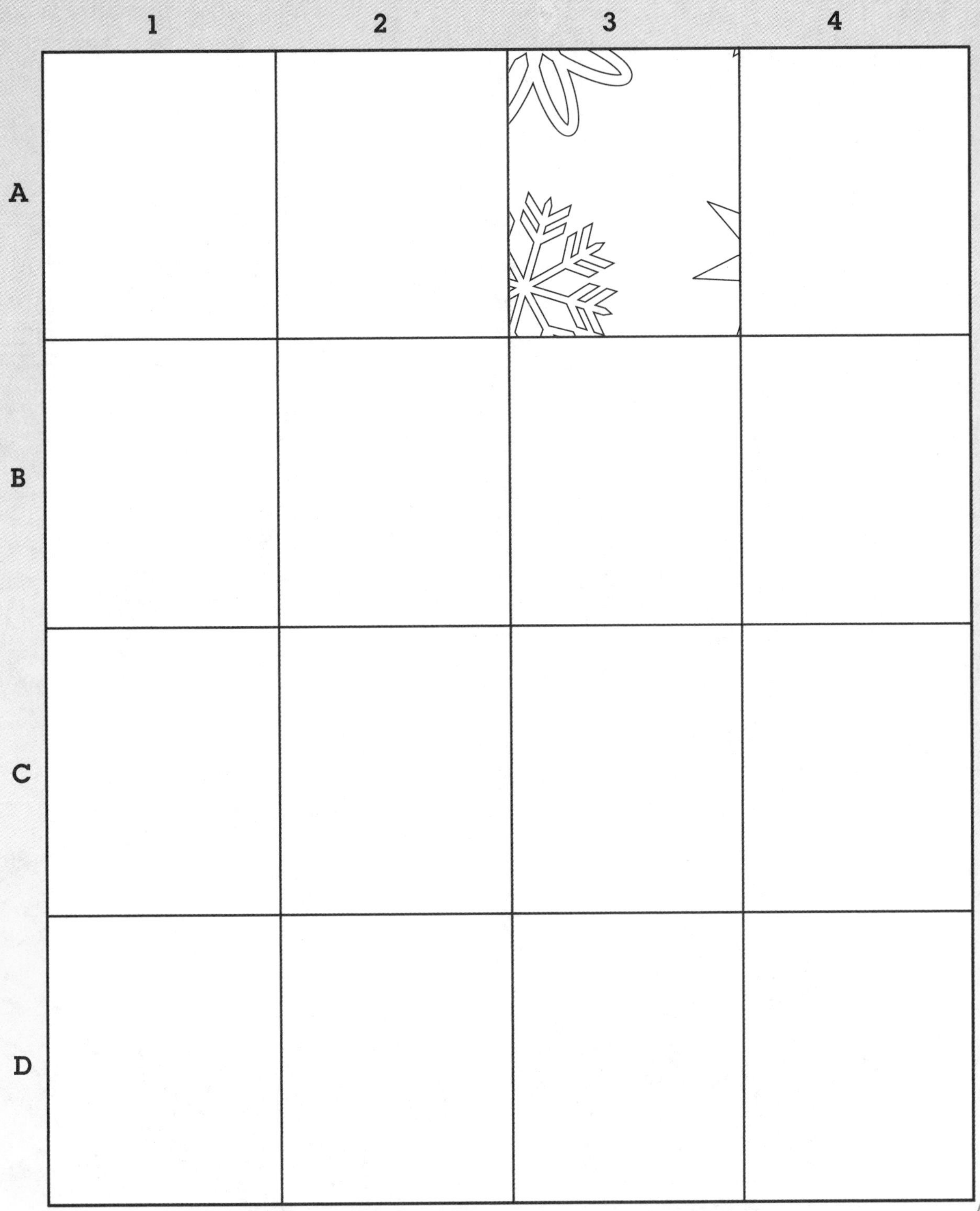

	1	2	3	4
A				
B				
C				
D				

Illustration: Amy Langendoerfer

CROSSWORD RIDDLE

Fill in these boxes with the letters of the words that answer each clue or description. When you've completed the grid, rearrange the letters in the yellow and blue boxes to answer our riddle.

ACROSS

1. Finish between second and fourth
5. Single choices, _____ one of those
7. First trio of letters in the alphabet
10. Groups of three, as in letters or singers
12. Opposite of *NW* on a compass
13. Abbreviation for *high school*
14. Short form of *tricycle*
17. Another word for *ocean*
18. 2, 4, and 6 are this type of number.
20. Number of dwarfs who met Snow White

DOWN

2. Listens to
3. Abbreviation for *Delaware*
4. Number of kittens who lost their mittens
6. Open wide and say "_____"
8. Prefix meaning "two," as before *plane* or *centennial*
9. Small folding bed
10. Number of blind mice in the song
11. Abbreviation for *seniors*
12. To travel on rollers or ice
15. The middle two letters of *view*
16. Santa _____, New Mexico
19. Opposite points on the top and bottom of a compass

Answer on page 50

Every baseball batter fears these:

MATHMAGIC

Ask a friend to choose any even number between 2 and 20.

Give your friend any even number to add to the number he chooses.

Ask your friend to multiply the new total by 2.

Then ask your friend to divide the resulting figure by 4.

Have him subtract half of the original number.

Surprise your friend by revealing his current number.

Answer on page 50

Illustration: Marc Nadel

K-9

While waiting at the dog show, Tara played a game. She knew there were 19 dogs entered in the contest. Eleven of the dogs each had one owner. Each of the other 8 dogs had two owners present. Tara made a list of comparisons. She was then going to put in a > (greater than), < (less than), or = (equal) symbol for each choice. But her dog ran off and she had to go get him. Can you surprise her by filling in the symbols before she gets back?

Hint on page 47

Number of legs in the room		Number of arms in the room
Number of ears in the room		Number of eyes in the room
Number of paws in the room		Number of fingers in the room
Number of noses in the room		Number of tails in the room
Number of legs in the room		Number of ears in the room
Number of tails in the room		Number of people in the room

Illustration: Jerry Zimmerman

Answer on page 50

TOP DOLLARS

Each team of two has been saving money all week. Can you tell how much

Alice and Brad have 12 coins.
One-quarter of them are quarters.
Half of them are dimes.
The remaining coins are nickels.

Corey and Dennis have 12 coins.
One-third of them are quarters.
One-quarter of them are nickels.
One-third of them are dimes.
The rest are pennies.

Edward and Felicia have 12 coins.
Two of them are quarters.
Two-thirds of them are dimes.
The rest are nickels.

Answer on page 50

each team has saved and which team has the most money?

Hint on page 47

Gary and Holly have 12 coins.
Half of them are quarters.
One-third of them are pennies.
The rest are nickels.

Imogene and Jerry have 12 coins.
One-quarter of them are quarters.
Half of them are nickels.
One is a dime.
The rest are pennies.

Kelleen and Lily have 12 coins.
One-third of them are quarters.
One-quarter of them are dimes.
One is a nickel.
The rest are pennies.

Illustration: Anni Matsick

Dewey has some funny books in his library. To check one out, solve each problem. Then go to the shelves to find the volume with the number that matches each answer. Put the matching letter in the blank beside each answer. Read down the letters you've filled in to find the title and author of the book Dewey just finished reading.

Shelf labels	
M 13	N 14	Z 26	K 11

Illustration: Scott Peck

Answer on page 50

Hint on page 47

$19 - 6 =$ _____

$3 \times 3 =$ _____

$12 + 7 =$ _____

$38 \div 2 =$ _____

$11 - 2 =$ _____

$2 \times 7 =$ _____

$5 + 2 =$ _____

$11 + 8 =$ _____

$3 \times 5 =$ _____

$30 \div 10 =$ _____

$19 - 8 =$ _____

$14 + 5 =$ _____

$8 - 6 =$ _____

$5 \times 5 =$ _____

$22 \div 2 =$ _____

$8 - 3 =$ _____

$8 + 6 =$ _____

$2 \times 10 =$ _____

$12 \div 2 =$ _____

$11 - 2 =$ _____

$9 + 5 =$ _____

$8 \div 2 =$ _____

$1 + 4 =$ _____

$16 - 3 =$ _____

SAND ART

Re-create this image without crossing over any lines or removing your pencil from the page.

Illustration: Barbara Gray

Answer on page 51

NOTHING BUT THE TOOTH

Dr. I. M. Painless is a busy dentist. Today she saw 14 children, all of whom have at least 1 missing tooth.

PATIENT'S NAME	NUMBER OF MISSING TEETH
Arthur	2
Bruce	3
Clark	1
Deanne	3
Emily	2
Fritz	4
Gary	1
Hal	1
Ilene	1
Jack	3
Kurt	2
Lori	2
Maggie	1
Nancy	2

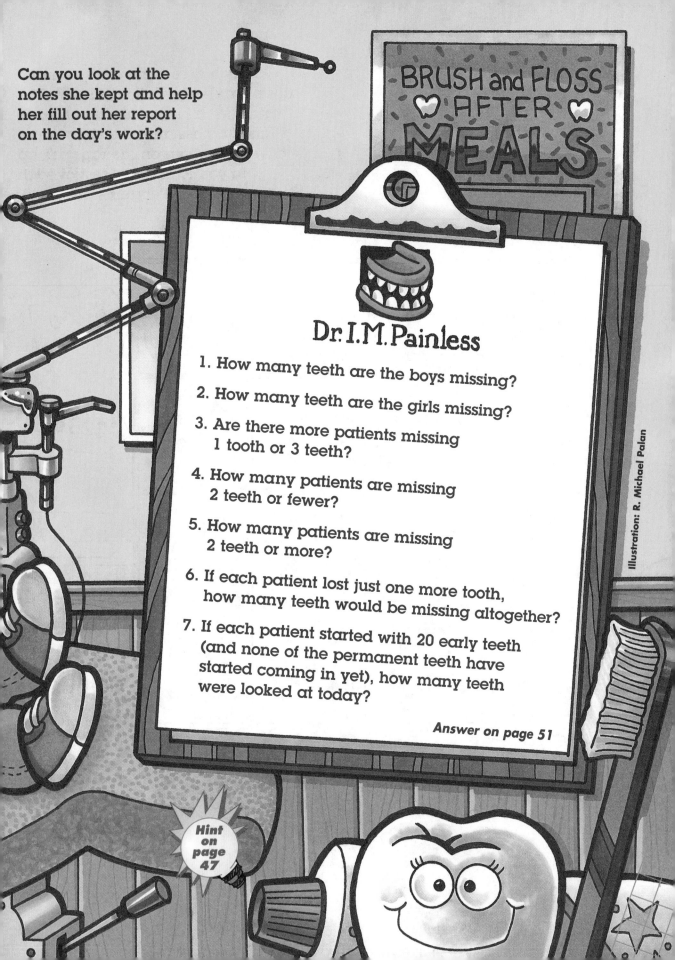

Can you look at the notes she kept and help her fill out her report on the day's work?

BRUSH and FLOSS AFTER MEALS

Dr. I.M. Painless

1. How many teeth are the boys missing?

2. How many teeth are the girls missing?

3. Are there more patients missing 1 tooth or 3 teeth?

4. How many patients are missing 2 teeth or fewer?

5. How many patients are missing 2 teeth or more?

6. If each patient lost just one more tooth, how many teeth would be missing altogether?

7. If each patient started with 20 early teeth (and none of the permanent teeth have started coming in yet), how many teeth were looked at today?

Answer on page 51

Hint on page 47

BEAN COUNTERS

Each type of beanbag animal costs a different dollar amount. The totals for all four animals on each shelf across and in each column down are given on the tags. It's up to you to find the cost of each animal. Penguins are $8.00.

Hint on page 47

$17.00

$28.00

$20.00

$26.00

$24.00

$22.00

$23.00

$22.00

Illustration: Marc Nadel

Answer on page 51

COLOR BY NUMBERS

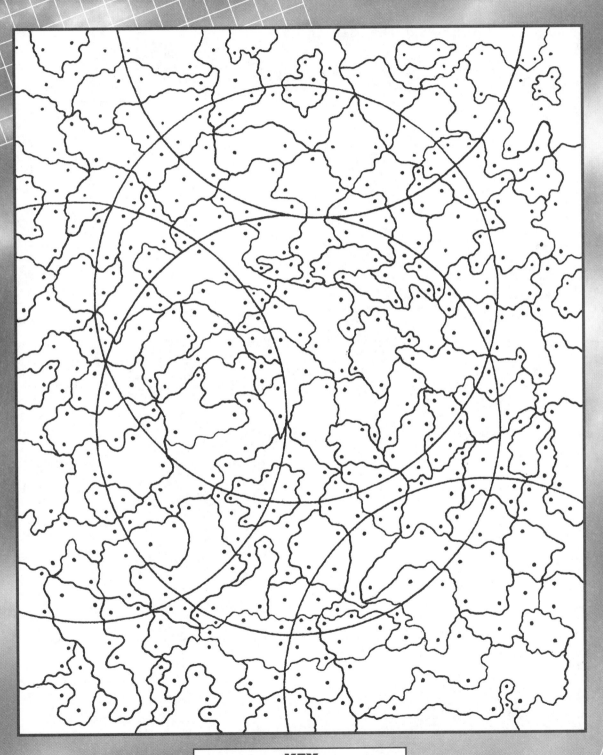

Illustration: Rob Sepanak

KEY
Even number of dots—Black
Odd number of dots—White

TREES

I think that I shall never see
A _____ lovely as a tree.

These words are from "Trees" written by Joyce Kilmer. To find the word that belongs in the blank, follow the instructions in each section. When you're

14	21	52
18	9	20
13	29	26
40	11	7
56	12	10

1. Shade the numbers that become greater than 90 when multiplied by 7.

Type of tree that begins with this letter: _____

20	55	52
74	54	66
71	36	125
93	6	99
19	82	47

Illustration: David Helton

2. Shade the numbers that become greater than 325 when multiplied by 6.

Type of tree that begins with this letter: _____

42

Answer on page 51

done, read each letter you've created in order to finish the quote. As a bonus, see if you can name a tree that has the same initial letter as the letter you've created in each section.

30	41	26
92	25	10
55	80	31
36	20	4
47	28	99

3. Shade the numbers that become greater than 100 when multiplied by 4.

Type of tree that begins with this letter: _____

72	56	93
66	90	87
71	86	77
90	63	68
70	19	91

4. Shade the numbers that become greater than 650 when multiplied by 10.

Type of tree that begins with this letter: _____

DESIGNER MATH

Example:

2

5 50

5

When multiplied, the numbers 2, 3, or 5 equal the numbers shown in the hexagons. Place a combination of those three numbers in the yellow triangles that surround each hexagon to equal the number in the shape. You can use 2, 3, or 5 more than once in each grouping.

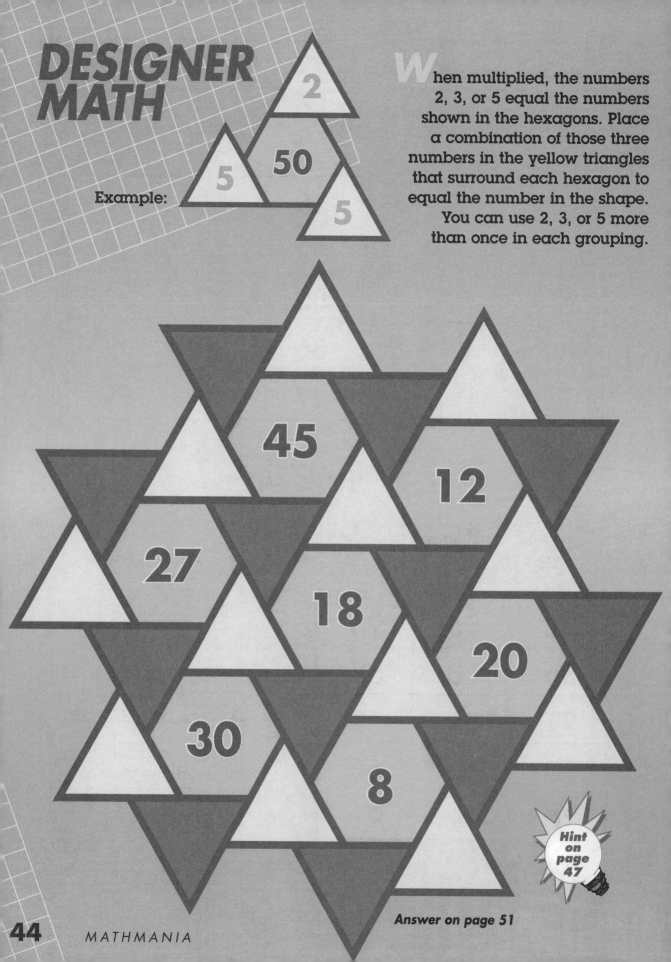

45

12

27

18

20

30

8

Hint on page 47

Answer on page 51

ROW, ROW, ROW

Each square contains a problem that has something in common with the two others in the same row across, down, or diagonally. The common element may be in the problem, or it may be in the answer. For example, in the top row across, each answer is an even number. Work the problems and then look at each row to find the common element. Do the part in the parentheses first.

$32 + 18 =$	$23 - 17 =$	$4 \times 5 =$
$106 + 6 =$	$231 - 114 =$	$(5 \times 5) \times 5 =$
$8 + 4 =$	$27 - 9 =$	$3 \times 7 =$

Answer on page 51

HINTS AND BRIGHT IDEAS

*T*hese hints may help with some of the trickier puzzles.

COUNT THE CROP (page 3)
Look for clues that show how you can count a group of tomatoes at a time. Then add in any loose ones.

SPECIAL DELIVERIES (pages 4-5)
Work all problems from left to right.

STRAIGHT RUNS (page 6)
Consecutive numbers are numbers that follow right after the other, such as 1, 2, 3, or 25, 26, 27. If you divide the sum you are working with by 3, you will always get the middle number of the sequence.

WONDER WINDOW (page 7)
Some shapes involve more than one pane of the window.

STACKING STANLEY (page 10)
Use a ruler to measure the length of the boxes.

IT'S ABOUT TIME (pages 12-13)
Use the size of each word as a clue to where it might fit. Then look for letter combinations to make sure you have connected the right words. Finding all the words on the clock before you fill in the grid may be the best way to start.

PHONE AGE (page 14)
Jed is 12 and his phone number is 211-0422 (2 + 1 + 1 + 4 + 2 + 2 = 12).

SQUARE 100 (pages 16-17)
Start in the lower left corner. You need to fill in only one number to make those four squares equal 100.

DIGIT DOES IT (pages 20-21)
The word *Inspector* appears in the note's greeting. Use the code numbers from this word to help figure out the rest of the message.

GOOD FENCES (page 22)
Before you count posts, you must figure out the length of each side of this square garden. What number times itself will give you 100 square feet? Now, if the kids want to space out their fence posts at a certain length, how many will they need?

A DIRTY JOB (page 23)
There are 2,000 pounds in a ton.

CROSSWORD RIDDLE (pages 30-31)
Each answers 5 Across. *N* is at one point of a compass.

K-9 (page 33)
There are 19 dogs and 27 people.

TOP DOLLARS (pages 34-35)
Half of 12 is 6. One-third of 12 is 4. One-quarter of 12 is 3.

LIBRARY LAUGHS (page 36)
Remember to consult the books to find the letter that matches each number.

NOTHING BUT THE TOOTH (pages 38-39)
To find the answer to question 7, multiply the number of patients by 20. Then subtract the total number of missing teeth.

BEAN COUNTERS (page 40)
The penguins are the most expensive. Look at the bottom row across to get started.

DESIGNER MATH (page 44)
The three numbers surrounding the 8 are all the same.

ANSWERS

STACKING STANLEY (page 10)

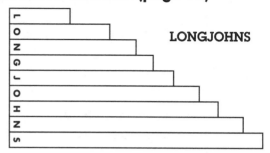

LONGJOHNS

COVER

There are 27 people in line.

COUNT THE CROP (page 3)

114 (9 × 12 = 108; 108 + 6 loose ones = 114)

SPECIAL DELIVERIES (pages 4-5)

5 × 5 + 5 = 30	7 × 5 = 35
41 – 8 – 2 = 31	40 – 4 = 36
16 + 16 = 32	44 – 7 = 37
11 × 3 = 33	10 + 19 + 9 = 38
20 + 14 = 34	14 + 13 + 12 = 39

STRAIGHT RUNS (page 6)

1. 5, 6, 7   3. 23, 24, 25
2. 12, 13, 14   4. 29, 30, 31

BONUS QUESTION: The numbers
are 1, 2, and 3. The total is 6.

WONDER WINDOW (page 7)

There are more triangles. We found more than
100 triangles and fewer than 100 squares.

ZOO CLUES (pages 8-9)

Alligator: How's by Zoo gives 1 to Can Zoo.
Python: Watt's Zoo and Because of Zoo each
    give 1 to How's by Zoo.
Toucan: Because of Zoo gives 2 to Can Zoo.
Gorilla: How's by Zoo gives 1 to Because of
    Zoo. Can Zoo gives 2 to Because of Zoo.
Elephant: Can Zoo gives 1 to How's by Zoo,
    and Watt's Zoo gives 1 to Because of Zoo.
    Or Can Zoo gives 1 to Because of Zoo, and
    Watt's Zoo gives 1 to How's by Zoo.
Giraffe: Watt's Zoo gives 3 to How's by Zoo,
    and Because of Zoo gives 2 to Can Zoo.
    Or Watt's Zoo gives 2 to How's by Zoo and
    1 to Can Zoo, while Because of Zoo
    gives 1 to How's by Zoo and 1 to Can Zoo.
    Or Watt's Zoo gives 1 to How's by Zoo and
    2 to Can Zoo, and Because of Zoo gives 2
    to How's by Zoo.

DOTS A LOT (page 11)

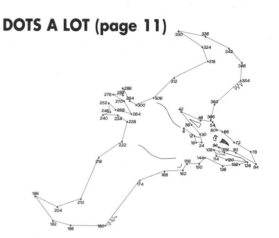

IT'S ABOUT TIME (pages 12-13)

TOMORROW
ZONE ... MORNING ... HISTORY
PAST ... FUTURE ... DATES ... RECENT
MOMENT ... TIME ... YESTERDAY
... SPRING ... DAWN
PRESENT ... HOUR
PERIOD ... SUNSET ... GAUGE
NOW ... WEEK ... SECOND
... CALENDAR

PHONE AGE (page 14)

Sylvia, age 14   802-1005
Oliver, age 15   521-0600
Jaime, age 7   233-1202
Lara, age 8   410-2102
Ari, age 11   203-0002
Bruce, age 12   310-0050
Lola, age 9   202-4000
Joel, age 16   614-3001
Nate, age 10   321-1103
Ellis, age 13   401-3121

GRAPHIX (page 15)
Which is the largest ant in the world?
ElephANT

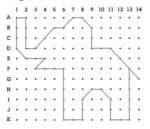

SQUARE 100 (pages 16-17)

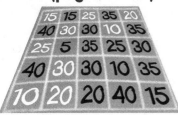

CUTUPS (page 18)
Jackie will make eight cuts. The final cut will give her two pieces.

BUSY DAY (page 19)
7:40 a.m. Wake up. Put on sweats—should take 5 minutes.
           Walk the dog (15 minutes).
8:00 a.m. Eat breakfast.
8:15 a.m. Shower and get dressed. Put wash into machine before leaving.
8:30 a.m. Leave for 45-minute drive to Beverly's house.
9:30 a.m. Help Beverly paint her room—should take 3 hours.
12:30 p.m. Go to lunch for an hour.
           Write letter to Carl (30 minutes).
2:05 p.m. Go home.
3:00 p.m. Go shopping with Mom—should take 90 minutes.
           Get haircut (45 minutes).
5:20 p.m. Weed front garden—should take 40 minutes.
           Hang out the wash (10 minutes).
6:10 p.m. Write thank-you note to Mrs. Tillson—should take 5 minutes.
           Wash cars (1 hour).
7:15 p.m. Eat dinner with family.
7:40 p.m. Wash dishes—should take 20 minutes.
           Walk the dog (15 minutes).
8:15 p.m. Leave for the movies.
10:30 p.m. Come home and go to sleep. Big day tomorrow!

DIGIT DOES IT (pages 20-21)
Dear Inspector Digit,
So they sent the cream of the cops after me. How sweet. But my trail will be cold before you stick anything on me. I even left 29 ice-cream sticks behind so you won't pop after me.
Rocky Rhodes

a-5	f-17	l-16	r-15	w-22
b-21	g-20	m-19	s-18	y-6
c-10	h-9	n-8	t-7	
d-11	i-3	o-2	u-1	
e-4	k-12	p-13	v-14	

GOOD FENCES (page 22)
4 (10 × 10 = 100 square feet)

A DIRTY JOB (page 23)
16 trips (2,000 × 6 = 12,000 pounds; 12,000 ÷ 750 = 16)

AN AMAZING WOMAN (pages 24-25)

Sarah Josepha Hale wrote the poem "Mary Had a Little Lamb."

DIFFERENT DEFINITIONS (page 26)
WEEKDAYS: THE ONES THAT AREN'T AS STRONG AS SATURDAY OR SUNDAY

PATTERN POSSIBILITIES (page 27)
A. 18. Each number on the bottom half is twice as much as the number directly opposite.
B. 22. Each number increases by 3, 6, 9, and 12.
C. 10. The sum of each overlapping oval is 19.

SCRAMBLED PICTURE (pages 28-29)

CROSSWORD RIDDLE (pages 30-31)

Every baseball batter fears these:
THREE STRIKES.

MATHMAGIC (page 32)

Your friend's final number will be exactly half of the even number you gave him in step 2.

K-9 (page 33)

Number of legs in the room (130)	>	Number of arms in the room (54)
Number of ears in the room (92)	=	Number of eyes in the room (92)
Number of paws in the room (76)	<	Number of fingers in the room (270)
Number of noses in the room (46)	>	Number of tails in the room (19)
Number of legs in the room (130)	>	Number of ears in the room (92)
Number of tails in the room (19)	<	Number of people in the room (27)

TOP DOLLARS (pages 34-35)

Alice and Brad:
3 quarters = $.75
6 dimes = $.60
3 nickels = $.15
Total: $1.50

Gary and Holly:
6 quarters = $1.50
4 pennies = $.04
2 nickels = $.10
Total: $1.64

Corey and Dennis:
4 quarters = $1.00
3 nickels = $.15
4 dimes = $.40
1 penny = $.01
Total: $1.56

Imogene and Jerry:
3 quarters = $.75
6 nickels = $.30
1 dime = $.10
2 pennies = $.02
Total: $1.17

Edward and Felicia:
2 quarters = $.50
8 dimes = $.80
2 nickels = $.10
Total: $1.40

Kelleen and Lily:
4 quarters = $1.00
3 dimes = $.30
1 nickel = $.05
4 pennies = $.04
Total: $1.39

Gary and Holly have the most money.

LIBRARY LAUGHS (page 36)

$19 - 6 = 13$	M		$8 - 6 = 2$	B
$3 \times 3 = 9$	I		$5 \times 5 = 25$	Y
$12 + 7 = 19$	S		$22 \div 2 = 11$	K
$38 \div 2 = 19$	S		$8 - 3 = 5$	E
$11 - 2 = 9$	I		$8 + 6 = 14$	N
$2 \times 7 = 14$	N		$2 \times 10 = 20$	T
$5 + 2 = 7$	G		$12 \div 2 = 6$	F
$11 + 8 = 19$	S		$11 - 2 = 9$	I
$3 \times 5 = 15$	O		$9 + 5 = 14$	N
$30 \div 10 = 3$	C		$8 \div 2 = 4$	D
$19 - 8 = 11$	K		$1 + 4 = 5$	E
$14 + 5 = 19$	S		$16 - 3 = 13$	M

MISSING SOCKS by Kent Findem